paper doll
Fashion Fun
Designer Sketchbook

★ American Girl®

Published by American Girl Publishing, Inc.

Copyright © 2007 by American Girl, LLC

Questions or comments? Call 1-800-845-0005,
visit our Web site at **americangirl.com**,
or write to Customer Service, American Girl,
8400 Fairway Place, Middleton, WI 53562-0497.

Printed in China
07 08 09 10 11 12 LEO 10 9 8 7 6 5 4 3 2

Editorial Development: Carrie Anton

Art Direction and Design: Camela Decaire

Production: Kendra Schluter, Gretchen Krause, Mindy Rappe,
Jeannette Bailey, Judith Lary

Photography: Radlund Photography; p. 46, beads and buttons, Salisbury Studios

Stylists: Pam Retelle, Amanda Crary

Special thanks to: Megan Boswell, Shelley Cornia, Lori Dresen, Annie Nguyen

Dear Doll Lover,

Feed your passion for fashion by creating one-of-a-kind styles for your paper dolls. Here's your chance to design a pretty party dress, a summery skirt, perfect pajamas—and more!

Follow your designing dreams using the templates and ideas in this book to inspire new outfits. Then send your styles down the runway in your very own paper-doll fashion show!

Your friends at American Girl

turtleneck

v-neck

cap

short

cropped sweater

7
Sleeve

¾ length

6
Top

cheerleader

long

What's Inside

Learn how to start smart with the book and supplies.

Each of the design pages shows basic clothing pieces that can be turned into different looks. We've given you four ideas for each, but there is no limit to how many styles you can create. Use the blank pages after the designs to sketch some of your own style ideas.

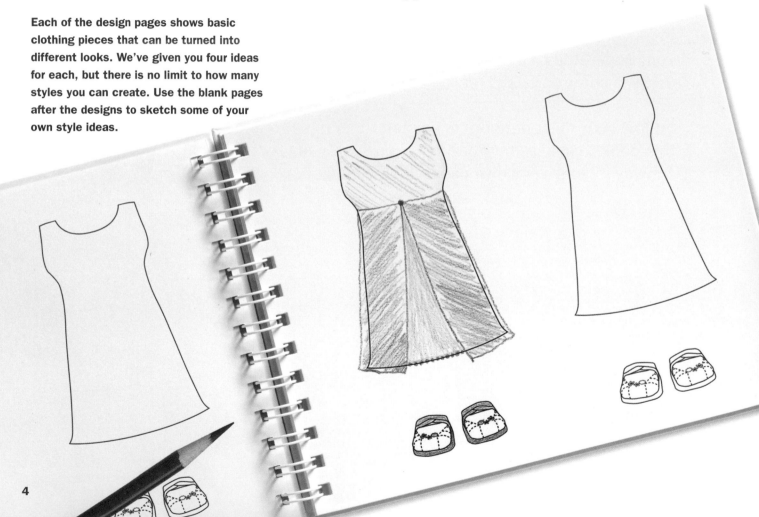

Fabric-Print Paper

Your kit contains 20 sheets of double-sided paper, and each side is made to look like fabric. That means you can make your doll a a paper skirt to wear to school, and then flip the skirt over for a new pattern she can wear on a sunny summer day.

Style Stencils

To make the paper into clothes, use the four Style Stencil sheets in your kit. We show you how on pages 6 and 7.

Paper Dolls

Show off the styles you create by dressing one of your three paper dolls in your designs. The reusable sticky dots allow you to swap clothing pieces to create as many outfits as you can imagine.

Finishing Touches

Jazz up your styles by adding fun finishing touches with the sequins, cording, and stickers in the kit. You can also add lots of other stylish stuff such as fabric, glitter, beads, and lace, which you can find at a craft store. Need ideas? See the last few pages of the book for ways to do up your designs!

Style Stencils

See how one stencil sheet can help you create so many different styles!

Just as a *seamstress*—or someone who sews clothes—uses a pattern to make clothes, you can use the four sheets of Style Stencils we've provided to trace and create your own paper fashions. Each stencil is based on an outfit you can find in the book but also can be changed to create the exact look you like.

Shirts

This book features tops galore, from T-shirts to turtlenecks! Use the Style Stencils to make collars, change sleeve lengths, and add details you like about one shirt to another shirt.

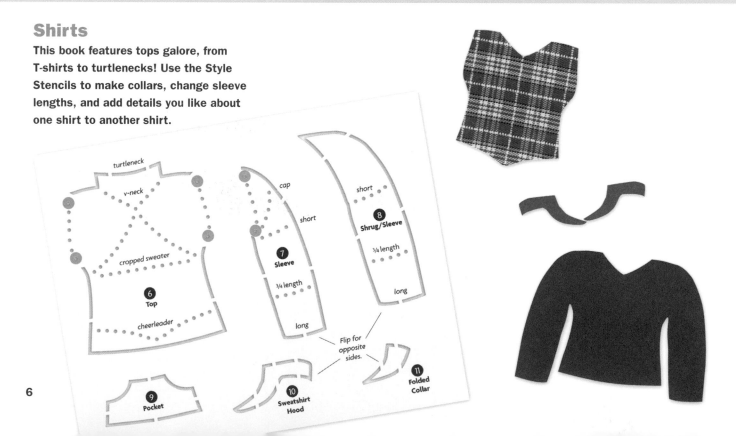

turtleneck

v-neck

cropped sweater

6
Top

cheerleader

cap

short

7
Sleeve

¾ length

long

short

8
Shrug/Sleeve

¾ length

long

Flip for opposite sides.

9
Pocket

10
Sweatshirt Hood

11
Folded Collar

Dress

The shift dress on page 18 is perfect to use in so many places. Shorten the length and add sleeves to create a tunic top. Add long sleeves and buttons on the front for a cool coat. Swap in short sleeves and a fun pattern for a nightgown.

Leotard

A leotard doesn't have to be just about dance. Use the top to make a tank or find a fun fabric to style a swimsuit.

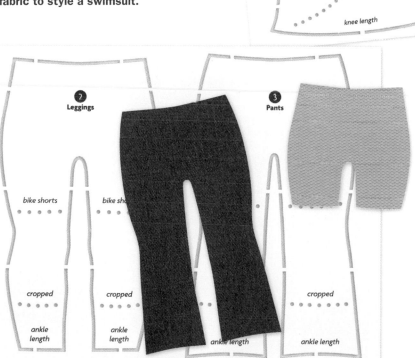

Pants

Don't limit yourself to denim when using the jeans pattern on page 14. Use this Style Stencil to make pants in all kinds of patterns. You can also follow the holes on the stencil to make capris or shorts.

Put It Together

Learn how to use the stencils!

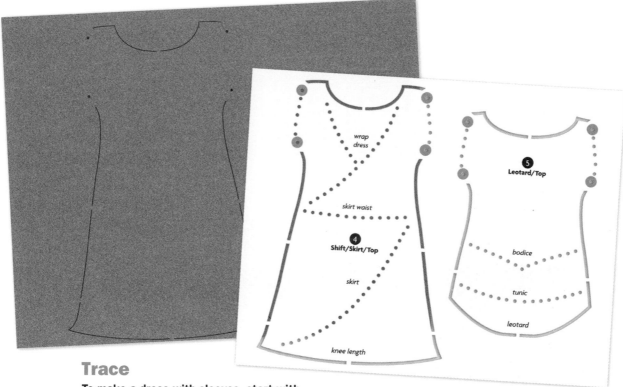

Trace

To make a dress with sleeves, start with
Style Stencil 4. Using a pencil, trace the
lines of the basic dress. Lightly fill in the top
and bottom holes only of each sleeve. If you
do not want sleeves, fill in all of the holes.

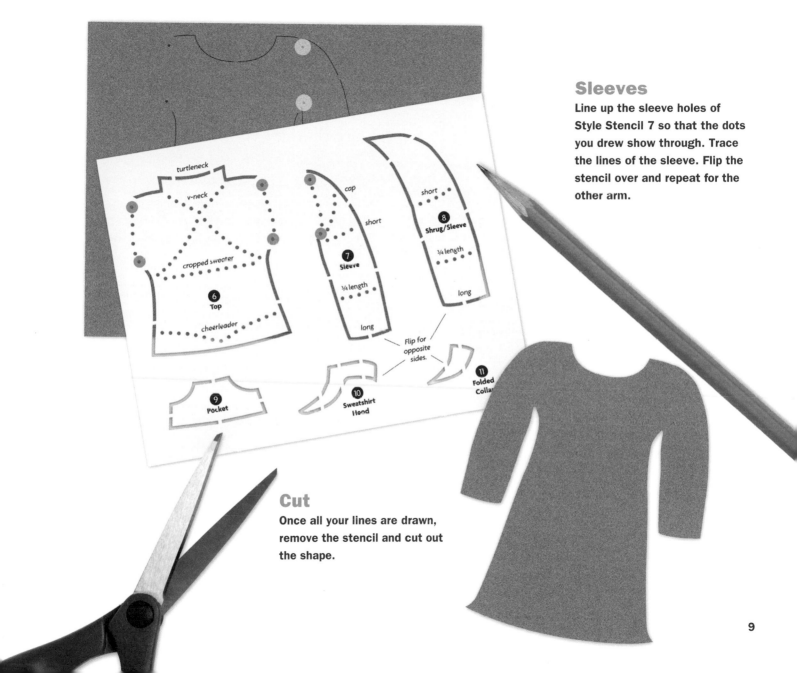

Sleeves

Line up the sleeve holes of Style Stencil 7 so that the dots you drew show through. Trace the lines of the sleeve. Flip the stencil over and repeat for the other arm.

turtleneck

v-neck

cap

short

short

8
Shrug/Sleeve

cropped sweater

7
Sleeve

¾ length

6
Top

cheerleader

¾ length

long

long

Flip for opposite sides.

9
Pocket

10
Sweatshirt Hood

11
Folded Collar

Cut

Once all your lines are drawn, remove the stencil and cut out the shape.

9

Fun with Fabric

Learn which fabrics—from corduroy to velvet—are right for your fashions!

If you've ever walked into a fabric store, you know that there are many kinds of fabrics to choose from. Fabrics are made from fibers—cotton or wool—that are spun into yarns before they are knit or woven into cloth. But not all fabrics are right for all types of clothing. In your kit, you will find papers that give the looks of lots of different fabrics and prints. Learn a little about each one to pick the perfect styles to go with your doll designs.

Corduroy is a heavy fabric that has textured ribs, which look a lot like ridges on a potato chip.

Faux fur (pronounced "foe" fur) is a synthetic material that looks like animal fur.

Denim is best known because of blue jeans—even though denim comes in more colors than just blue!

Eyelet is easy to recognize by its decorative holes, which form flowers and other fun patterns. You can usually find eyelet in white, cream, and pastel colors.

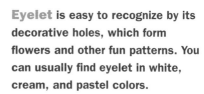

Flannel, often made from cotton, is soft and warm and is used for things such as pajamas and cold-weather shirts.

Herringbone is a fabric that looks as if it is made of all zigzags.

Jersey Is a plain knitted fabric that can be made of wool, cotton, nylon, rayon, or silk. For a sample of cotton jersey, check out a T-shirt.

Knit fabric has a bit of stretch to it and has all types of uses. The knit fabric paper included in your kit is like a wool knit used for sweaters.

Lace is a decorative fabric that is often used as trim on collars, cuffs, and hemlines.

Plaid is an easily recognizable pattern of different-sized stripes crossing over one another to make blocks.

Suede is a leather fabric that has been brushed to give a soft texture.

Tulle (pronounced "tool"), a net-like fabric, has lots of tiny holes in it. It is used for tutus, petticoats, and veils.

Velvet is a smooth, soft material that is great to use when making party dresses for cold-weather occasions.

Put your clothes to the test!
See if you can find any of these fabrics in your closet.

Color Creations

Change a style with a simple spin of the color wheel.

A Whole Lot of Hues

If you have a bright blue sweater or a pair of purple pants that you love to wear, then you know that even if the clothing is comfy, the color is what makes it your favorite. Color can help you create different looks even if you're using the same clothing pattern.

For a fun look, try going *monochromatic* by using one color for the whole outfit—the trick is to use different shades of that color.

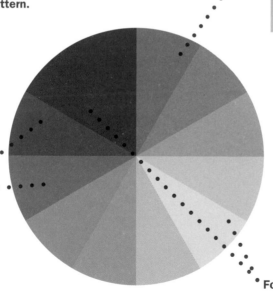

For a colorful look that's not too loud, use *analogous colors,* such as purple and blue, or colors next to each other on the color wheel.

For a bold look, use *complementary colors,* which pair up opposite colors on the color wheel.

Colors for Every Season

Color not only changes the look but also can determine in which season something should be worn. Fashion designers often pick warm colors for the spring and fall and cool colors for summer and winter.

Warm colors have yellow and red *under-tones,* which are the base colors. Spring colors are light warm colors such as peach, ivory, and pale yellow. Fall colors are darker hues, such as gold, tomato red, and brown.

Cool colors have blue undertones. Summer colors are light cool colors and include lavender, pale green, and sky blue. Winter colors, such as midnight blue, deep purple, and emerald green, are dark.

Cool for School

Flowers and fringe are an A+ combo for funky fashion.

Give denim a splash of style by drawing on flowers with a gel pen.

Sweatshirt: stencils 6, 7, 9, 10, and flower shape
Jeans: stencil 3

Show your spirit with coordinating stripes and reverse-fold pants in your school's colors.

Turn a pullover hoodie into a jacket by drawing in a zipper.

Sweatshirt: stencils 6, 7, 9, and 10
Jeans: stencil 3

14

Show your style smarts when you turn casual school looks into outfits that really make the grade.

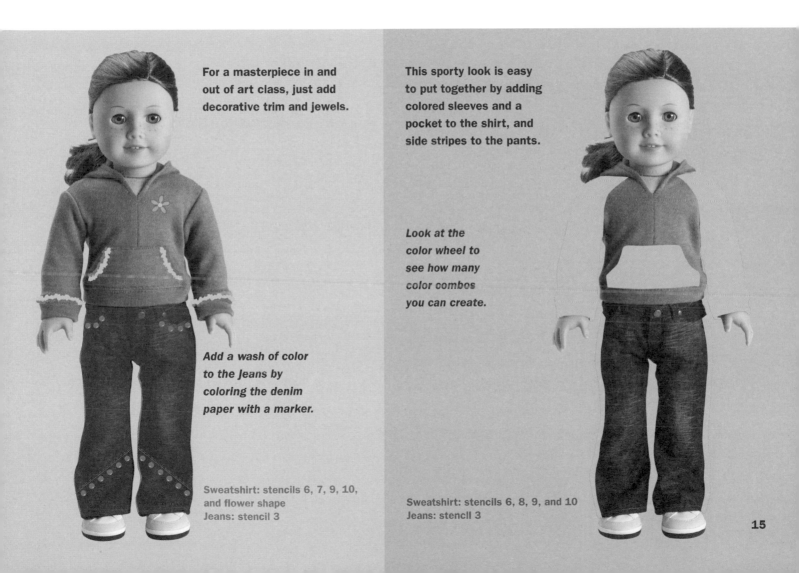

For a masterpiece in and out of art class, just add decorative trim and jewels.

Add a wash of color to the jeans by coloring the denim paper with a marker.

Sweatshirt: stencils 6, 7, 9, 10, and flower shape
Jeans: stencil 3

This sporty look is easy to put together by adding colored sleeves and a pocket to the shirt, and side stripes to the pants.

Look at the color wheel to see how many color combos you can create.

Sweatshirt: stencils 6, 8, 9, and 10
Jeans: stencil 3

Now design your own styles!

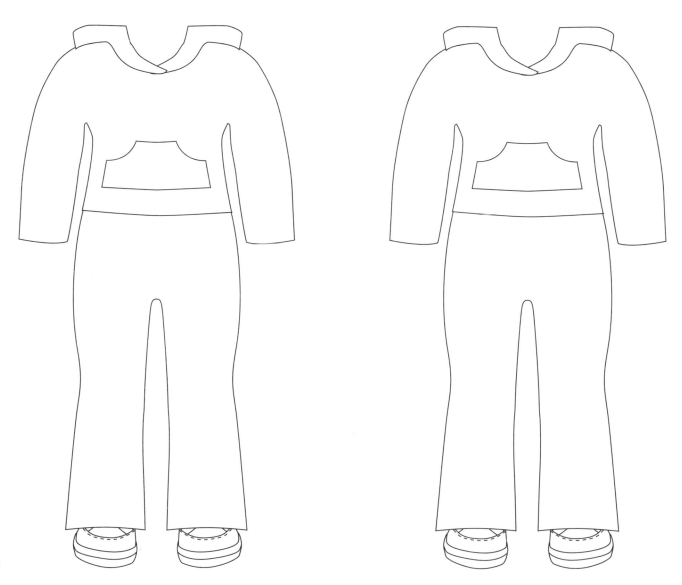

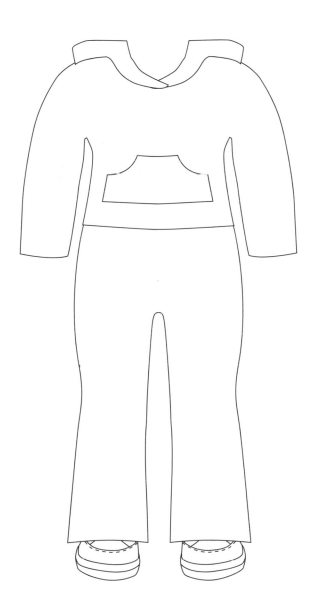
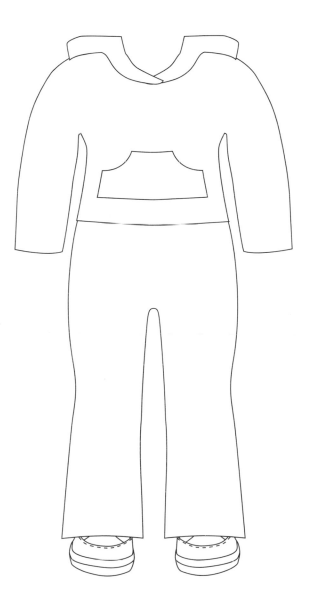

shift into Spring

Make this shift petal perfect with a few flowers and an extra layer of fabric—or tissue paper—for a full skirt.

Change this outfit by using other shapes in place of the flower details.

Dress: stencil 4
Skirt: bottom of stencil 4 and flower shape

This dress is spot on with polka dots, long sleeves, and a bow belt tied to make an empire waist.

An empire (pronounced "ahm-peer") waist is simply a high waist.

Dress: stencils 4, 7, and flower shape

See how buttons, sleeves, and collars can change the shape of this simple shift dress.

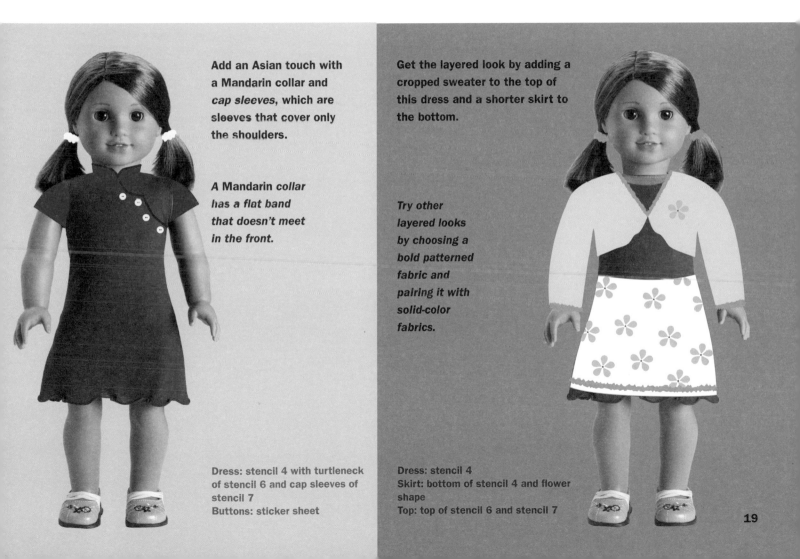

Add an Asian touch with a Mandarin collar and *cap sleeves*, which are sleeves that cover only the shoulders.

A Mandarin collar has a flat band that doesn't meet in the front.

Get the layered look by adding a cropped sweater to the top of this dress and a shorter skirt to the bottom.

Try other layered looks by choosing a bold patterned fabric and pairing it with solid-color fabrics.

Dress: stencil 4 with turtleneck of stencil 6 and cap sleeves of stencil 7
Buttons: sticker sheet

Dress: stencil 4
Skirt: bottom of stencil 4 and flower shape
Top: top of stencil 6 and stencil 7

Now design your own styles!

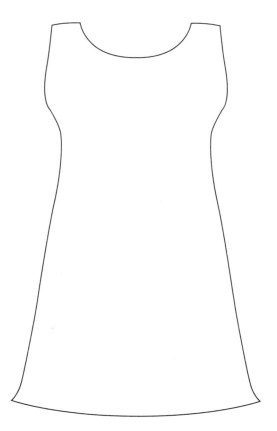

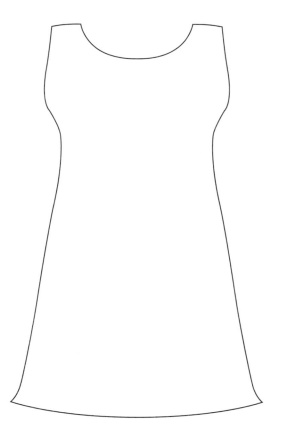

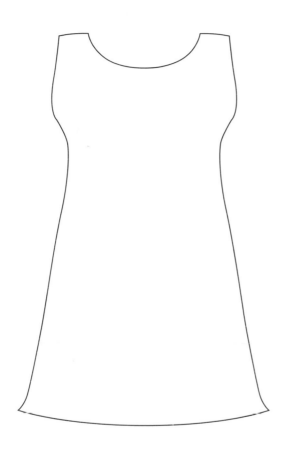

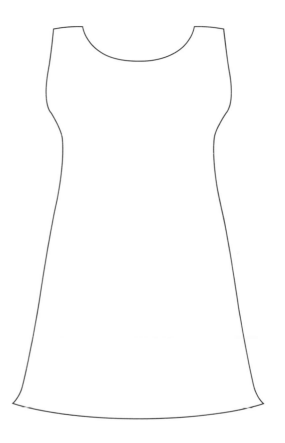

Make a fashion statement with a collarless cropped jacket and criss-cross boots.

Look smart with an argyle sweater vest and boots in a matching color.

Make a jacket from a long-sleeved shirt by cutting an opening in front.

To make pleats with paper, cut out two skirts. From the bottom of one, cut out five V shapes. Then place that skirt on top of the other one.

Turtleneck: stencils 6 and 7
Jacket: stencils 6 and 7
Skirt: bottom of stencil 4

Turtleneck: stencils 6 and 7
Vest: top of stencil 4
Skirt: bottom of stencil 4

It's easy to look casually cool when you add different layers to a basic top and pleated print skirt.

Wrap it up with a cropped wraparound sweater that matches the flowers on the skirt.

Make the clothes look real by drawing fold lines where fabric should be gathered or bunched.

A poncho is the perfect piece to pair with a coordinating skirt and cute boots.

Ponchos are similar to small blankets with an opening in the center to slip over the head.

Turtleneck: stencils 6 and 7
Sweater: top of stencil 6 and stencil 8
Skirt: bottom of stencil 4 and flower shape

Turtleneck: stencils 6 and 7
Skirt: bottom of stencil 4
Poncho: top and bottom lines of stencil 5, outside lines of ¾-length sleeve of stencil 7 (connect all lines)

Now design your own styles!

Designed to Dance

Look perfect in purple while you practice!

Use a see-through paper, such as tissue paper or vellum, to make the skirt.

Leotard: stencil 5
Skirt: bottom of stencil 4 and circle shape
Shrug: stencil 8
Tights: stencil 2
Leg warmers: bottom of stencil 2 (cut wavy lines along each side)

Combine a black tutu with lace and sparkles for a show-stopping costume.

Use tissue to make a tutu. Gather the long side of the tissue paper so that it is as wide as the doll's waist. Stick the tutu to the doll and puff her skirt to make a bell.

Leotard: stencil 5 and circle shape
Tutu: see instructions above
Tights: stencil 2

These different dance outfits are sure to get a standing ovation!

Jazz up a ballet outfit by adding a fringed skirt and bow tie.

To make fringe from paper, cut strips 3/4 of the way up a band of the paper.

Leotard: stencil 5
Bowtie: sticker sheet
Skirt: bottom of stencil 4
Tights: stencil 2

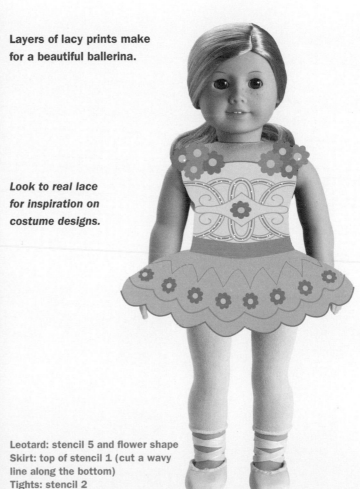

Layers of lacy prints make for a beautiful ballerina.

Look to real lace for inspiration on costume designs.

Leotard: stencil 5 and flower shape
Skirt: top of stencil 1 (cut a wavy line along the bottom)
Tights: stencil 2

Now design your own styles!

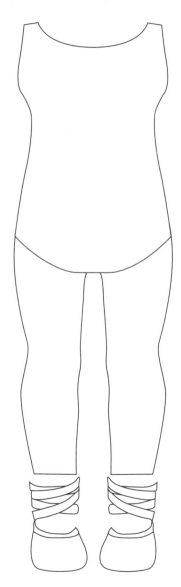

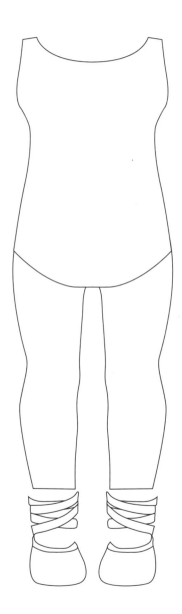

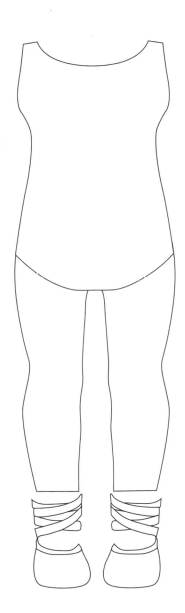
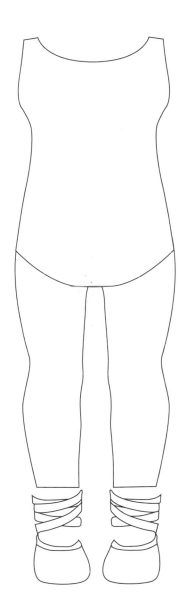

Split the top in two with your team colors. Finish the look with matching socks.

Make a pleated skirt by folding the paper like an accordian.

Shirt: v-neck of stencil 6 and star shape and stencil 7
Skirt: top of stencil 1

For a cheerful style, just add pom-poms.

To make paper pom-poms, cut fringe into two same-size strips of paper in different colors. Roll the paper and tape closed.

Shirt: v-neck of stencil 6 and star shape
Skirt: top of stencil 1
Pom-poms: see instructions above

Give three cheers for these high-energy uniforms!

Add a number or logo to your jersey that says you're #1!

Create a collar in one of your team's colors for a winning look.

Shirt: stencils 6, 7, and 11
Shorts: top of stencil 3

A long-sleeved soccer jersey is perfect goalie gear!

Block out your jersey with color patches and sleeves in your team colors.

Shirt: stencils 6 and 7
Shorts: top of stencil 3

Now design your own styles!

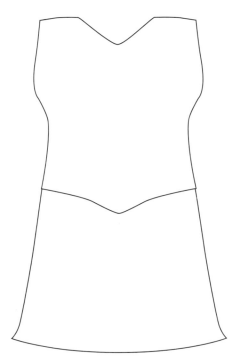

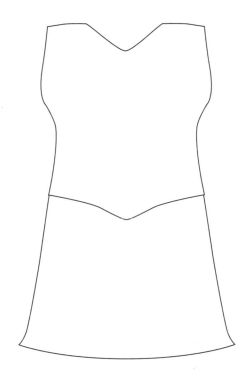

Sweet Dreams

Edge your outfit with bold colors for loungewear that is anything but lazy.

Check the color wheel for more sleepwear shades.

Add a fluffy robe to warm you up right at night.

Add long sleeves and a front opening to the shape of the shift stencil to make a robe.

Shirt: stencils 6, 7, and 11
Buttons: sticker sheet
Pants: stencil 3

Robe: stencils 4 and 7
Pants: stencil 3

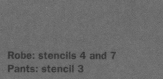

Here are four pairs of PJ's that are anything but a snore!

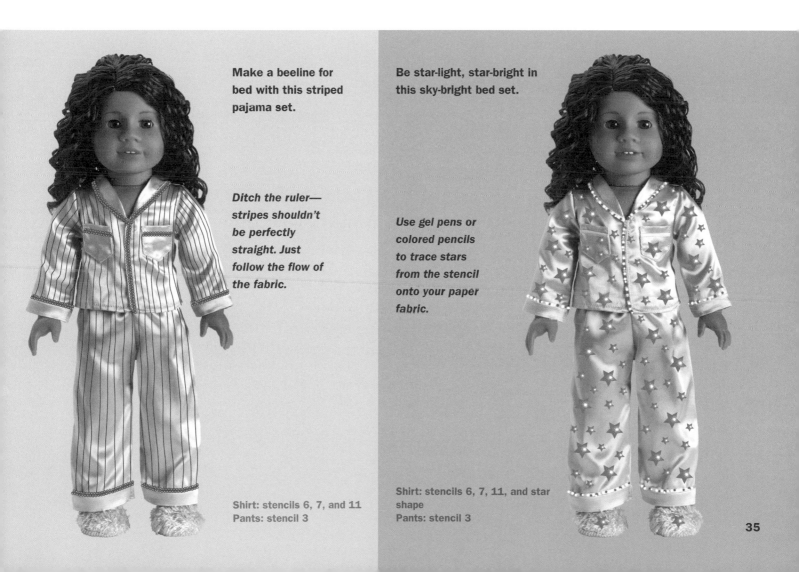

Make a beeline for bed with this striped pajama set.

Ditch the ruler—stripes shouldn't be perfectly straight. Just follow the flow of the fabric.

Shirt: stencils 6, 7, and 11
Pants: stencil 3

Be star-light, star-bright in this sky-bright bed set.

Use gel pens or colored pencils to trace stars from the stencil onto your paper fabric.

Shirt: stencils 6, 7, 11, and star shape
Pants: stencil 3

Now design your own styles!

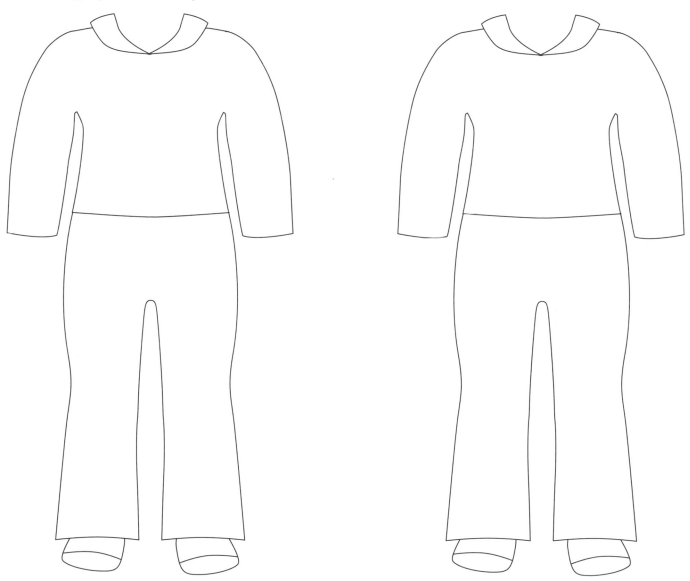

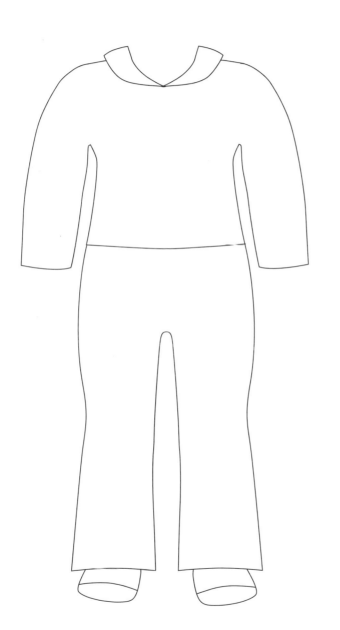
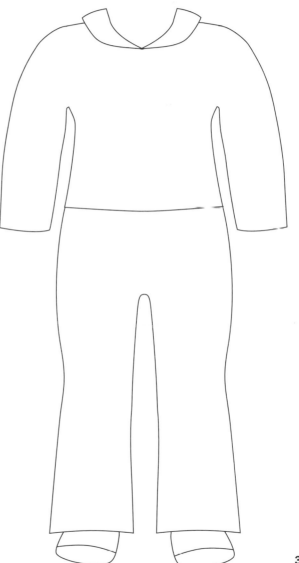

All Dolled Up

Beauty blossoms when flowers are drawn onto this divine design. A *shrug*, which is just a shawl with sleeves, completes this party-perfect dress.

Add a tiara from the sticker sheet to top off this look.

Top: bodice of stencil 5
Shrug: short sleeves of stencil 8
Skirt: stencil 1

Ruffles are the right look for any special event—and sparkles make it even better!

Ruffle your edges by drawing wavy lines before cutting them out.

Top: bodice of stencil 5
Skirt: stencil 1

Be the belle of the ball with these four fancy fashions.

Give your dress some sparkle by using silver paper circles as jewels.

A bodice *is the top of a fitted dress.*

Top: bodice of stencil 5 and circle shape
Skirt: stencil 1

Turn this party dress into a garden gown with spring-colored flowers made from paper.

Make your skirt look fuller by adding a wide belt in a contrasting color.

Top: bodice of stencil 5 and flower shape
Skirt: stencil 1

Now design your own styles!

Celebrate in Style

Turn the top into a side-tie top with coordinating trim.

Use the holes on the stencil as a guide for the lines of this top.

Shirt: top of stencil 4 and stencil 7
Skirt: top of stencil 1
Headband: sticker sheet

A belt, a necklace, and fancy cuffs show that this design is all about the details.

A cuff is the material in the wrist area of the sleeve.

Shirt: top of stencil 4 and stencil 7
Skirt: top of stencil 1
Belt and necklace: sticker sheet

A perfect party outfit is all about the details.

Celebrating is as easy as adding spots of sparkle.

The dots on this dress can be made with paper, craft jewels, sequins, or fabric paint.

Shirt: top of stencil 4, stencil 7, and circle shape
Skirt: top of stencil 1

Waves aren't just for the beach! Add them to a party outfit as part of a cool new pattern.

Instead of waves, add different shapes of paper, or draw shapes on with a gel pen.

Shirt: top of stencil 4 and stencil 7
Skirt: top of stencil 1
Barrettes: sticker sheet

Now design your own styles!

Crafty Clothing

Take your fashions beyond paper by getting crafty with your designs!

On the next few pages, see what you can do with paper and then what you can do to dress up your designs with things from around your home and materials from a craft store. You can turn paper outfits into works of art using fun stuff like fabrics, ribbon, yarn, and much more!

Supply List

Here are some supplies that you can use when making your designs more craft-astic!

Beads
Bells
Buttons
Construction paper
Cording
Cotton balls
Crayons
Fabric
Fabric paint
Feathers
Felt
Foam paper
Gift ribbon
Glitter
Glue stick
Hole punch

Lace
Markers
Patches
Pipe cleaners
Pom-poms
Ribbon
Rubber stamps
Scissors
Sequins
Scrapbook paper
Stencils
Stickers
String
Trim
Wrapping paper
Yarn

Not Just a Button

You can use anything to create crafty clothes. For example, a real button can be used to make a polka-dot pattern, as the center of a flower design, or as a belt buckle. And when you need to make buttons on your paper doll's clothing, buttons that fit your real clothing will most likely be too big. Instead, use a pen or fabric paint to draw on buttons, or try sticking on beads, stickers, or sequins.

Paper Version

Supplies:
Paper fabrics in kit
Colored pencils

Crafty Version

Supplies:
Fabric
Decorative trim
Sequins
Stickers
Scrapboook paper
Ribbon
Beads

47

Paper Version

Supplies:
Paper fabric in kit
Tissue paper in kit
Marker
Gel pen
Paper punch

48

Crafty Version

Supplies:
Fabric
Decorative trim
Lace
Ribbon
Cording
Beads
Jewels

Paper Version

Supplies:
Paper fabrics in kit
Star-shaped paper
punch or star stencil
Glue

Crafty Version

Supplies:
Fabric
Beads
Stickers
Fleece
Pom-poms

Paper Version

Supplies:
Paper fabrics in kit
Star stencil
Colored pencil

Crafty Version

Pom-poms:
Wrap yarn around
a small cardboard
square. Slip the
yarn off and tie the
bundle at one end.
Snip open one side
and fluff.

Supplies:
Felt
Fabric
Stickers
Cording
Gift ribbon
Scrapbook paper
Yarn

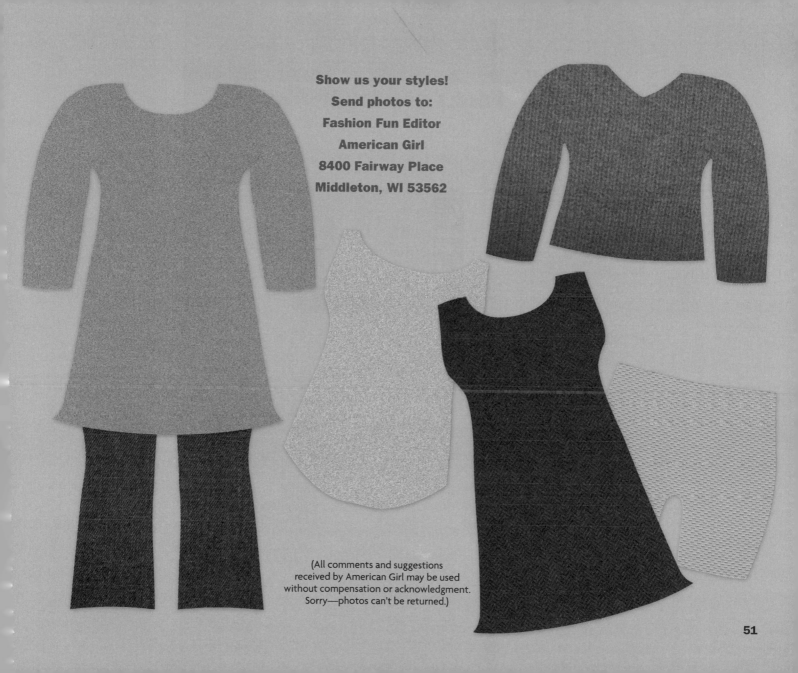

Show us your styles!
Send photos to:
Fashion Fun Editor
American Girl
8400 Fairway Place
Middleton, WI 53562

(All comments and suggestions
received by American Girl may be used
without compensation or acknowledgment.
Sorry—photos can't be returned.)

Here are some other American Girl books you might like:

❑ I read it.

❑ I read it.

❑ I read it.

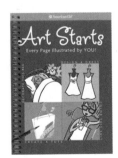

❑ I read it.

❑ I read it.